Th

A Play For Young People

by

Aidan Chambers

HEINEMANN EDUCATIONAL BOOKS
LONDON

Heinemann Educational Books Ltd
LONDON EDINBURGH MELBOURNE AUCKLAND TORONTO
SINGAPORE HONG KONG KUALA LUMPUR
IBADAN NAIROBI JOHANNESBURG
LUSAKA NEW DELHI

ISBN 0 435 23166 9

Published by
Heinemann Educational Books Ltd
48 Charles Street, London W1X 8AH
Printed Offset Litho and bound in Great Britain by
Cox & Wyman Ltd, London, Fakenham and Reading

For Martin

PRODUCTION NOTES

Like *Johnny Salter* which preceded it, *The Car* was written for the young people of Archway School, Stroud. As in *Johnny Salter*, I tried to leave plenty of scope for the young players to create the characters in their own way. Certain scenes have been left deliberately skeletal. The schoolgirls belonging to MISS SHORT-BOTHAM and the FOREMAN and his men need only a lively imagination to provide them with personalities and stage business that will make them enjoyable to perform and entertaining and meaningful to watch. The fights and antics of PAUL and his 'lot' are left open in this way too. One warning, however. The balance in this play between broad comedy and the near tragedy of LUKE's predicament is delicate. If either extreme is over-emphasized in production the play will fail.

The car appears, in cold print, an insuperable technical difficulty. We found, in the original production, that it was not only exciting but surprisingly easy to mock up an old car in wood and hardboard, with 'spare part' attachments collected from scrap-yards. The 'trans-formed' car of the second act is then easily engineered by attaching prepared templates on to the old car body during the interval.

I am always happy to hear from people interested in these plays, and to help where I can with problems of production. I can be reached via the publishers.

A.C.

The Car was first produced by Archway School, Stroud, on 7th December, 1966.

CHARACTERS

SIMON
PAUL
PIPPA
CHIPS
WALLY
WILLY
LOO
EDDIE
LUKE
MAGISTRATE
POLICEMAN
MRS LOVEJOY
EARL
MISS SHORTBOTHAM
LILLY
CAMELIA
PRUNELLA
AMANTHA
CLERK
MISS FLUTTERBODY
FOREMAN
1ST COUNCILMAN
2ND COUNCILMAN
3RD COUNCILMAN
SAM LAWSON
MAGGIE LAWSON

ACT ONE

Music: a haunting tune, with that capacity for joy with a hint of sadness often in Irish melodies. The lights create a fine spring day.

A quarry with a ragged sky-line. Paths drop down to the pit of the quarry, in which lies an abandoned car, not vintage, but with an unfashionable look to it.

The day fully lit, we hear above the melody, the sound of voices in a chasing game. They dodge about somewhere just over the sky-line.

A boy appears, panting. Breathless for a moment, he hangs on to the broken handrail that guards the only dangerous drop into the quarry. He is about thirteen, hardy, and will be strong when he is fully grown. He looks about for a hiding-place, sees the car, looks for pursuers, then drops skilfully on to the quarry floor and dives into the car. He has hidden too hurriedly and doesn't realize that his bottom is sticking up in view. The music has faded away.

There is a pause before a tall thin boy appears on the sky-line. PAUL *is about fourteen. He gazes about, sees the car and* SIMON'S *bottom sticking out. He smiles, turns, whistles, waves, indicates 'Over here' and makes a sign to be quiet.*

After a moment, he is joined by a little fellow who is always pulling faces (CHIPS); WILLY *and* WALLY, *inseparable pals;* PIPPA, *a solid, capable girl;* LOO, *her friend, who is much afflicted by adolescence.*

PAUL *indicates* SIMON. *The others nod and warm to the fun.*

They descend by various ways to the quarry floor. PAUL *directs them round either side of the car, which they surround with elaborate care, closing in.*

EDDIE *has come on to the sky-line. He sits on a projecting rock, taking no part in the game. He fiddles with something, and though he seems one of the gang, he never takes any part in what they do.*

PAUL *looks round, a look that asks 'All ready?' They nod. With an ear-splitting yell, they jump on the hidden* SIMON. *There is a struggle. Finally* SIMON *emerges and runs for a path out of the quarry. The others anticipate him. There is a chase accompanied by much shouting. At last* SIMON *is caught and pinned down by* WILLY *and* WALLY, *driven against the radiator of the car.* PAUL *stands away, victorious and in command.*

PAUL: You ran.

WILLY: Scared.

WALLY: Daren't face the music.

CHIPS: Expect we'll have to kill you.

LOO: They're at it again. If they start again, Pippa, I'm going home.

PIP: They're just playing, Loo. Stop champing.

CHIPS: Yes, stop champing. Don't know why we don't kill you!

He tries to frighten her with his Dracula face.

PAUL: Shut up, Chips. Simon is more important. He ran.

WILLY: Rules say mustn't run.

WALLY: Never.

PAUL: Do we all agree that Simon ran?

ALL (*not* EDDIE *or* LOO): Yes.

LOO: No. I don't. Stupid game.

    CHIPS *tries to frighten her again.*

PAUL: Then he must suffer the penalty.

SIMON: Not here, Paul. It's all stony.

PIP: No, Paul. Not here.

PAUL: His fault. Shouldn't have run here.

LOO: Might as well leave them alone, Pip. Brainless, all of them.

PIP: But it isn't fair. Not here. It's terribly stony and he'll get hurt.

WALLY: Ask Eddie.

PAUL: Is it fair, Eddie?

EDDIE: He ran. Rules say mustn't leave the lower field. He did. So he's got to face the penalty. I thinks it's fair.

    WILLY *and* WALLY *hold* SIMON *while* CHIPS *tries to take* SIMON's *shoes.* SIMON *thrusts him away.* PAUL *comes to help but is knocked away by* SIMON's *feet again. There is a struggle and a chase, until* SIMON *is at last brought down and held by* PAUL, WILLY *and* WALLY, *while* CHIPS *takes the shoes. The girls and* EDDIE *sit watching.*

    When CHIPS *is safely away,* SIMON *is released. The shoes are passed about while* SIMON *tries to catch them. But he is puffed and the stony ground is painful. Finally, the passing game takes them over the sky-line, leaving* SIMON *nursing his feet by the down-stage back wheel of the car.*

    Enter LUKE. *He is fifteen, sun-tanned, dirty, long-haired. He has been living rough for some days. He comes confidently to the car, not having seen* SIMON. *He sits in the driving-seat, pulls out a bundle of sandwiches and is just about to take a huge bite when* SIMON *groans.* LUKE *starts, locates the noise, is about to run, reconsiders, adopts a superior air and speaks.*

LUKE: And who are you, my lad?

SIMON *starts, yells in fright, jumps aside, yells at the pain in his feet, and collapses a few feet from the car.*

SIMON: You scared me.

LUKE: Sorry, I'm sure.

SIMON: Who are you? You weren't here when they took my shoes.

LUKE: I'm Jack the Ripper. Who are you?

SIMON: I'm Simon.

LUKE *(eating ravenously)*: What they take your shoes for?

SIMON: It's the rules. Just a game we play in the field.

LUKE: So what do they take your shoes for?

SIMON: I dunno. Just do. It's always been the penalty.

LUKE: Sounds daft to me.

SIMON: Might sound daft, but it isn't when it happens.

SIMON *watches* LUKE *eating.*

SIMON: You hungry or something?

LUKE: Yeah. Haven't had anything for days. Well . . . not since yesterday anyhow.

SIMON *(unimpressed)*: Oh!

LUKE: On the road, you see.

SIMON: Which road?

LUKE *(laughing)*: Which road! Hark at him! Not any road, mate. Just *the* road. You know – on the move.

SIMON: Oh. Where?

LUKE: Not anywhere, mate. That's just it. I just go where I like. Go anywhere.

SIMON: Oh – tramping!

LUKE *crumples the bag and throws it away. He wipes his nose with a great sniff on his sleeve, rubs his hands and stretches.*

LUKE: Like to come into my car?

SIMON: *Your* car! That old thing's been there for ages.

LUKE: Maybe. But it's mine now. I've slept here for three nights.

SIMON: Whatever for?

LUKE: Fun, mate. You aren't half thick!

Noise of the gang returning. They stop short when they see LUKE *in the car, and stare at him.* LUKE *is unabashed. He poses in ridiculous fashion, as for a magazine.*

LUKE: Like to take a photo, would you?

PAUL: Who are you, then?

SIMON: Jack the Ripper.

CHIPS: Jack the Ripper? (*He approaches the car cautiously, peering at* LUKE *all the time.*) Don't look much like Jack the Ripper to me!

LUKE: The name's Luke. Who are you?

The gang come towards him.

PAUL: I'm Paul. He's Chips. We call him that because he's so small and thin.

WILLY: I'm Willy.

WALLY: And I'm Wally.

CHIPS: They're always together.

PAUL: This is my sister. Her name's Pippa, but we call her Pip for short.

CHIPS: And that's what she gives you more often than not – the pip!

LUKE: Comedian!

PAUL: That's Pip's friend. Her name's Loo.

LOO (*coy at the stranger*): Hello!

LUKE: The sullen one's Simon. Met him already. Who's the other one?

CHIPS: That's Eddie.

WILLY and WALLY: Eddie.

PAUL: Eddie doesn't say much.

LUKE: So I notice.

CHIPS: But he knows a lot.

LUKE: I'll believe that when I hear it. Well, now the formalities are over, come and join me in my car.

WILLY: *Your* car!

They are all astonished and want to laugh.

WALLY: Been there for ages.

SIMON: That's what I told him but he says it's his now.

LUKE: So it is.

They climb up around him.

CHIPS: Don't see how it can be yours if it was here long before you.

SIMON: Says it's his because he slept in it for three nights.

PAUL: Have you?

LUKE (*pleased by his success so far – the gang are fascinated by him*): Yeah. Sure.

WALLY: Crumbs!

WILLY: Cripes!

LOO: Oh, lor! He's like the rest of them – mad.

CHIPS: What for?

LUKE: What for, what for?

CHIPS: What for you want to sleep here three nights for?

LUKE: Because I like cars and I like sleeping, that's what for.

SIMON: Says he's on the road.

PAUL: On the road?

LUKE: On the road.

WALLY: How do you mean, on the road?

LUKE: You know, you're all as bad as simple Simon there. I'm tramping about. Walking. Touring. On Shanks's pony.

LOO: You mean you're just walking about the place?

LUKE: Yeah.

LOO: On your own?

LUKE: Yeah.

LOO: Without any adults?

LUKE: Lord, yes.

LOO: Just for fun?

LUKE: Just for fun.

LOO: That proves he's mad. Don't think we ought to have anything more to do with him. We'll probably all catch it.

WILLY: Catch what, Loo?

LOO: Madness. It's contagious.

PAUL: Are you really just tramping about the place?

LUKE: Cross my heart and hope to die.

PIP: And your parents let you?

LUKE *eyes* PIP *a moment.*

LUKE: Course. Why not?

PIP: Ours wouldn't.

CHIPS: How old are you then?

LUKE: Fifteen and over.

SIMON: Then why aren't you working?

LUKE *climbs out of the car and crosses to* SIMON.

LUKE: Simon, old lad, there's things you just ain't understood yet.

SIMON: Like what, for instance?

LUKE: Like, for instance, that there's more to life than just working all day.

CHIPS: That's what I told our mum the other day – but she still made me do the washing-up.

LUKE: Never mind, Chips. When you're my age, the world changes.

PAUL: Well, all I can say is you've got some pretty unusual parents. And why sleep in this old thing?

LUKE: Told you – because I like cars and I like sleeping. Always have. So when I saw this one here I thought, Luke, old chap, that's just the place for a bed. Out of the way. Roof over your head if you want it. More comfortable than the ground. And you never know – you might get it to go.

SIMON: Get it to go!

He looks mockingly at LUKE *a moment, then bursts into gales of laughter. The others join in.* LUKE *is peeved at first, but then his cocksureness returns.*

LUKE: Don't you be so sure it can't be done.

PAUL: This old thing! But it hasn't gone for months. That's why it's been chucked here.

They still find the idea funny and are wandering on to the sky-line as though to exit.

SIMON: Anyway, who'd want to make it go?

They all turn to hear LUKE'S *answer.*

LUKE: Us maybe.

SIMON: Us!

More laughter. LUKE *shouts them down.*

LUKE: Look. There's that poor old car, chucked away in this out-of-the-way place. Just cos nobody wants it. Can't be bothered to look after it properly. So they just chuck it away. Well, I think that's a bit off. I've

looked at the engine, and it ain't *that* bad – not so bad
it couldn't be made to go.

LOO: How do you know? Who told you about engines?

LUKE: My dad, that's who. My dad told me about
engines and I'm good with them.

WALLY: May be. But that car's falling to bits.

WILLY: To bits. Look at the body-work.

LUKE: Nothing some repairs and a tin of paint won't
put right. Wants a good clean more than anything.
(*He storms up to* PAUL.) Better than playing kids' games
and pinching each other's shoes. (*He snatches* SIMON*'s
shoes from* PAUL *and throws them to* SIMON.) This would
be something worth while. How about it? You lot
and me. I'll tell you what needs doing and you get the
stuff and help do it. (*The gang are looking round at each
other, beginning to be fired by* LUKE*'s enthusiasm.*) I'll
bet that when this car is done up and we get it to go,
we'll be able to sell it easy as pie to them folk that like
having old cars. Whatever we make we share. Fair
do's all round. How about it?

CHIPS: That's a good idea, Paul. I could do with a few
thousand pounds pocket money.

LOO: Be lucky if you make twopence each.

CHIPS: OO! Go back to your knitting!

PAUL: What do you think, Pip?

PIP: I'm not sure really. It might be fun. And we've
done nothing like it before. I can't see any harm in it.
But do you think we ought to tell our parents first
what we're doing?

CHIPS (*storming at Pip*): Tell parents! If you tell parents
you might as well give up before you start!

SIMON: The whole thing will be a waste of time anyhow.

WALLY: Then you suggest something better.

WILLY: Yeah. I'll bet you can't.

WALLY: Fed-up of playing kids games I am.

CHIPS: Me too.

PAUL: What does Eddie think?

> *Pause.*

EDDIE: Don't see why not. Reckon I could get some plugs and stuff from my dad.

WALLY: And I could get some paint.

WILLY: We've got some metal cleaner and some tools I could bring.

CHIPS: I could get some tyres.

PAUL: I could bring some spares from our garage. Pip and Loo could do some work on the upholstery.

PIP: It wouldn't be a very fine job, but we could do something.

LOO: I suppose so, Pip. But why do we always have to give the boys their own way?

PIP: Because they're boys, I suppose.

LUKE: There! I knew we could do it. Tell you what. Let's you go away and get what you can and bring it back here. I'll do a proper inspection and decide how to get the work shared out. Then we can make a start. How about that?

CHIPS: Smashing!

WALLY (*jumping up on to the bonnet*): Ladies and Gentlemen . . .

WILLY (*jumping up beside him*): Operation Car. . . !

> *The gang race off excitedly.* SIMON *limps off still disgruntled and not in favour of the idea.* EDDIE, *who has been glaring at* LUKE, *follows.*
>
> *As* EDDIE *goes,* LUKE *climbs into the car, obviously*

pleased. PIPPA *comes from behind the car where she hid when the others went off.* LUKE *is not aware of her until she walks to the front of the car.*

PIP: Hello.

LUKE's *smile vanishes. He is annoyed at being caught. He slumps down in the driving-seat, and turns away from* PIP.

LUKE (*brash*): Thought you'd all gone to get things.

PIP: The others have. I thought I'd stay and talk to you for a while.

A pause. LUKE *stares at* PIP.

PIP: Do you mind? ·

LUKE: Suppose not. Stay if you want.

A pause. Suddenly their eyes meet.

LUKE: What do you want to talk about then?

PIP: Nothing really. (*She smiles nervously at him.*) Just that it seemed odd finding you here and none of us know you. Do we? Not properly.

LUKE: Does it matter?

PIP: No.

LUKE: Well then?

PIP: Just that it's nice to know about people. Who they are and what they do and where they live and what they're like. Don't you think?

LUKE (*almost attacking her*): No! People are always fishing. Always wanting to know. Poking their noses into other people's lives. It's nothing to do with them. Why can't they leave other people alone? Nobody's hurting them. I don't want people to know me. I don't ask about you. Why should you ask about me?

PIP: It's only to be friendly. Don't you like that?

LUKE: O.K. So we're friends. You don't have to ask all sorts of snooping questions, do you?

PIP: Honestly, Luke, I wasn't snooping. But if you'd rather, we'll not talk about you.

LUKE: I'd rather.

Silence. LUKE *sits in the car again.* PIP *looks uncomfortably about.*

PIP (*trying to brighten up*): Wally's father owns a garage so I expect he'll bring all sorts of useful things. Will it take long, do you think? Doing up the car, I mean?

LUKE (*reluctantly*): No. Simple job. This car hasn't been like this long. My dad used to do up cars like this as easy as pie, and sell them for far more than he paid.

PIP (*sitting in the car next to him*): Your dad must be nice.

LUKE (*thawing somewhat*): Yeah. Great. He taught me how to drive. Before I was old enough. On the back roads, you know, where there wasn't any traffic and no police.

PIP: That must have been fun.

LUKE: Yeah. Terrific. First time I ever sat in the driving-seat for a session I jerked the gears. Dad had a thing about gears. 'You grate that gear?' he says. 'Yeah,' I says. 'Out you get,' he says. 'That's it!' And it was. Made me swap into the passenger-seat and he drove straight off home. It was mother put it right. Said dad hadn't to be so daft – anyone could make a mistake first time out.

PIP: Did he take you again?

LUKE: Yeah. A few days later. But I could feel him wince every time I jerked the gear. Funny about gears, my dad.

PIP: I'm a bit frightened of cars myself. They look like great mechanical monsters sometimes.

LUKE: First time I saw a car I ran. I was just little, mind, but I ran. Scared stiff I was. Thought it was some sort of horrible beastie. Just up and ran.

PIP: What happened?

LUKE: Oh, dad chased me. He couldn't understand it at first. But when I told him he laughed and said, 'Never run, boy.' (*He stops suddenly. The music is heard.* LUKE *stares ahead, as though seeing something invisible.*) 'Never run away.' Funny that. Never remembered that bit before. I remember he said that now.

He is unaware of PIP, *speaking as though to himself. She waits a moment, puzzled.*

PIP (*rising*): I'd better go after the others and help.

LUKE *is silent. The lights are fading, leaving only the car picked out.*

PIP: Be back soon. (*She goes up on to the sky-line.*) Bye.

PIP *exits.*

LUKE *stands, his eyes fixed now to the highest point of the quarry. He is cowering as though very nervous, and when he speaks his voice is younger and sullen.*

A cold spotlight comes up on the MAGISTRATE, *who is standing by the quarry handrail.* LUKE *is joined by a* POLICEMAN.

MAGISTRATE: You cannot go on running away. You must learn to face things like a man. I have taken into account all that the Children's Officer has said about you and the unfortunate circumstances of your background. But let this be a final warning to you. I will brook no more of your irresponsible behaviour. I am tempted to punish you severely and to send you to a higher court, recommending that you be sent to a Borstal institution, where you might be brought to your senses. However, neither the Children's Officer nor the Probation Officer think this right for you and I am willing to be guided by their advice. But this is the last occasion. Next time you will be more harshly treated. Do you understand?

LUKE: Yes, sir.

MAGISTRATE (*to* POLICEMAN): Call Mrs Lovejoy.

POLICEMAN (*calling off*): Mrs Lovejoy.

Enter MRS LOVEJOY. *She is middle-aged, a comfortable-looking woman, whispy-haired and heavily built. She carries her shopping bag.*

MAGISTRATE: Mrs Lovejoy, you are the boy's foster-mother, I believe?

MRS LOVEJOY: That's right, sir. And he'll do his best, I'm sure.

MAGISTRATE: I hope so. He cannot go on in the way he has.

MRS LOVEJOY: It's all that upset last year, sir.

MAGISTRATE: Quite, quite. But we must draw the line somewhere, Mrs Lovejoy. Are you absolutely sure you can manage the lad? Would it not be better for him to be in an institution or with a family where there is a man?

MRS LOVEJOY: I know I'm on my own, sir. But an institution would finish him, sir. He'd never survive there. Not for ten minutes. Not Luke. And I think it's too late for him to settle into a family now, sir.

MAGISTRATE: Very well, Mrs Lovejoy. He is your responsibility. I only hope you'll be wise and let the Probation Officer know at once if you need help.

MRS LOVEJOY: Of course, sir. I'm sure he'll do his best. Thank you, sir.

MAGISTRATE: Luke, you will be on probation for three years and in Mrs Lovejoy's care. Now heed my warning! You may step down.

The light on the MAGISTRATE *fades as he exits. The* POLICEMAN *exits. The music returns softly.* MRS LOVEJOY *crosses to* LUKE, *where they are pooled in light.*

MRS LOVEJOY: Hello, Luke.

LUKE (*unable to look at her*): Hello, Mrs Lovejoy.

MRS LOVEJOY: Good to have you back, Luke.

LUKE: Thanks. (*A pause. Then with an effort.*) Mrs Lovejoy . . . I'm sorry I went off like that. I . . .

MRS LOVEJOY: Don't you mention it, Luke. Not another thought. We all do daft things from time to time. Though it *is* silly to run away. (*She turns and walks away.*) You just come along with me. I've some sausage and chips for your tea and a slice of that favourite cake of yours . . .

MRS LOVEJOY exits, leaving LUKE in the car. As she goes the remaining spot and the music fade. There is a moment's blackout. Suddenly the lights return to daylight. EARL is standing at the top of the quarry. He gives an expansive cough.

EARL: Ah, 'tis a fine day to contemplate the world from such a lofty view.

LUKE comes to, and makes as though to run off.

EARL: Don't run off, young man. I'm not the Devil himself, merely his minion and not worth the effort of running from. Stay put, sir, stay put.

EARL walks into the quarry. He is a full-bearded tramp dressed in voluminous clothes that fall about him, which along with his beard and hat so cover him that it is difficult to pick out his features, except for his sharp and mobile eyes. There is jauntiness in his walk and sparkle in his voice. He stops by the car.

EARL: As I say, a fine and lofty view you have from here. I admire your choice of resting place. And whom have I the honour of addressing?

LUKE: The name's Luke.

EARL: And mine Earl. (*He shakes hands elaborately.*) Known by such to both my friends and my enemies. Makes life easier. You can love me and call me Earl, or you can hate me and call me Earl, and I shall never know the difference. Two names are a nuisance.

LUKE: Are you on the road?

EARL: I am, as you so delicately put it, young man, on the road. Not a respected nor much followed profession nowadays, but still (*he eyes the car*) one of great rewards. Is this your car?

LUKE: Yes, mine. Ours really. Some friends and me is doing it up, see?

EARL: Ah! You've friends. You and your friends?

LUKE: Friends? Yes . . . suppose so. (*The idea gives him pleasure.*) Yeah, me and my friends.

EARL: Indeed. Doing it up? How sad. Nothing is left to die comfortably and alone nowadays. Someone always wants to patch and mend. It's a bothersome world. Truly a pity. That car would have made a nice berth for the night.

LUKE: That's what I've been using it for – sleeping in.

EARL: Indeed? (*He stands looking, obviously waiting for an invitation to use the car too.*)

LUKE (*realizing at last*): Oh! You can share it if you like.

EARL: May I? What generosity! (*He climbs into the back seat.*) Yes, indeed. Two could manage comfortably. One in the front and one in the back.

LUKE: O.K. Only tomorrow my friends and me will be doing it up so you'll have to help or keep out of the way.

EARL: But of course. I never hinder. There's too much to do in the world to waste time hindering. I said to my last employer – I occasionally give of my services, you know? – I said to my last employer, I never hinder men at work. I'm glad to say he took the hint. He sacked me that night. Very accommodating chap like that. Said he wouldn't hinder me from moving on. (*He leans confidentially close to* LUKE.) There is, however, one problem with the generous arrangement we have just made.

LUKE: What's that?

EARL: The back seat is far more comfortable than the front.

LUKE: Then we'll have to take turns at sleeping in the back, won't we?

EARL: Admirable suggestion. Very sensible. I'd hate to deprive you of your sleep by leaving you in the front every night! (*They laugh together.*) Come, my friend. You must tell me about yourself. A young apprentice to the fellowship of the road – most unusual: at least in the professional sense. Plenty of these thumbers who cadge lifts and take rides. But *real* – pardon the expression – tramps! There's few of us left, and youngsters rarely join us nowadays.

Exit EARL *and* LUKE *in the direction of the village. A pause before the schoolmistress,* MISS SHORTBOTHAM, *enters. She is very young, a teacher just out of college, enthusiastic, but incompetent. She has the beginnings of authority but it is gained by the use of stock schoolmistress methods. She is dressed in the most modern fashion, quite inadequate for camping. She has a haversack on her shoulders. She steps daintily along the sky-line and surveys the view.*

SHORTBOTHAM: Just the place. A fine camping spot. And a super view. (*She calls off.*) Girls. Forward. This will do beautifully.

SHORTBOTHAM *moves into the quarry. Enter four schoolgirls:* LILLY, CAMELIA, PRUNELLA, *and* AMANTHA. *They are contrasting types, none of them particularly rigged out for camping. They are exhausted by the climb up the hill, but giggling and excited by the outing nevertheless. All, that is, except* AMANTHA, *who is bored and disgusted by the whole affair. She is very much a city girl and an embryo vamp.*

Once in the quarry they collapse noisily.

SHORTBOTHAM: Good. Good. A delightful situation. A pity about that disgusting piece of ancient machinery, which rather spoils the place, but I think you'll agree, girls, that this is a most pleasant spot for our first night's rest.

THE GIRLS: Yes, Miss Shortbotham. (*They pronounce it 'bottom'.*)

SHORTBOTHAM: Excellent. I knew you'd like it. Now, girls. Organization. We must specialize to be efficient. So – up we get!

The girls groan but get up with as much grace as they can muster.

SHORTBOTHAM: Now. Amantha.

AMANTHA: Yes, Miss Shortbotham?

SHORTBOTHAM: Will you collect enough wood to give us a fine open fire? After all, if we come into the great outdoors we must learn to be self-reliant, mustn't we? So off you go, Amantha. Wood!

Exit AMANTHA.

SHORTBOTHAM: Prunella.

PRUNELLA: Yes, Miss Shortbotham?

SHORTBOTHAM: You have the primus, I think?

PRUNELLA (*producing the primus from her haversack*): Yes, Miss Shortbotham.

SHORTBOTHAM: Then while Amantha is collecting wood, you may light the primus and boil a kettle so that we can have a nice cup of tea to cheer us in our toil. (*She giggles.*) A slight cheat, but never mind.

PRUNELLA (*holding the primus up and looking closely at it*): Yes, Miss. But I don't think I know how to use it.

SHORTBOTHAM: Don't you, dear? Neither do I. They didn't tell me anything about that in College. But never mind. It can't be difficult. Such a little machine. Just turn that round thing and light a match.

PRUNELLA: Yes, Miss.

SHORTBOTHAM: Over there looks a good place. By that unpleasant piece of abandoned automobile.

PRUNELLA *goes up-stage of the car and sits down behind it.*

SHORTBOTHAM: Now – Lilly and Camelia.

LILLY and CAMELIA: Yes, Miss Shortbotham?

SHORTBOTHAM: I want you to erect Camelia's tent so that we can find out how to do the others. Here will be admirable, I think. While you do that, I'll go off and aid Amantha. (*She crosses to* PRUNELLA.) *Do* be careful with that primus, Prunella. Just keep trying.

Exit MISS SHORTBOTHAM.

CAMELIA *has unpacked her tent.*

CAMELIA: You do the poles, Lilly, and I'll do the tent.

LILLY: Yes, Camelia. I've never done it before.

CAMELIA: It's simple. Just fit them into each other.

LILLY (*looking at the poles, puzzled*): Yes, Camelia.

CAMELIA *has rolled the tent out flat. She tries to reach inside for the hole where the pole will fit. She finds her arm is too short.*

CAMELIA: I can't reach the hole, Lilly.

She struggles. At last she puts the tent over her head. It envelops her completely. She stands, but trips on the folds of the tent and falls flat. She gets up.

CAMELIA: Where's the pole, Lilly?

CAMELIA *is searching about for* LILLY, *who has been trying to fit the poles together.* LILLY *at last finds the right ends and makes a complete pole.*

LILLY: Just coming, Camelia.

CAMELIA *is staggering about.* LILLY *picks up the tent and puts it over her own head.*

LILLY: Where are you, Camelia? Here's the pole. Camelia?

Both girls are covered by the tent now. Both are searching for each other. LILLY *swings round.* CAMELIA *finds herself spun in a wide circle as a result.* LILLY *turns the other way, which wraps* CAMELIA *round her.* LILLY *tries turning back. This throws* CAMELIA *staggering out of the tent. She is holding the pole with a surprised expression on her face. At this moment enter* MISS SHORTBOTHAM, *followed by* AMANTHA, *both carrying puny bundles of sticks.* SHORTBOTHAM *stops, horrified.*

SHORTBOTHAM: Camelia!

CAMELIA, *taken by surprise at the schoolmistresses yell, turns, trips and falls flat.*

SHORTBOTHAM: Lilly!

LILLY *attempts to escape from the tent, and falls over the folds. There is an explosion and smoke from the direction of* PRUNELLA *and the primus.* PRUMELLA *rises, her face black, and screams.* MISS SHORTBOTHAM *rushes up to her.*

SHORTBOTHAM: Prunella, what *have* you done?

PRUNELLA: Exploded, Miss Shortbotham.

SHORTBOTHAM: Stupid girl! Think what you might have done. Damaged your clothing, or the primus.

PRUNELLA (*still snivelling*): Sorry, Miss Shortbotham.

SHORTBOTHAM: Besides, it was very dangerous.

PRUNELLA: I didn't mean to explode. (*She breaks into more floods of tears.*)

SHORTBOTHAM: Now don't cry, dear. Come and help.

SHORTBOTHAM *and* PRUNELLA *cross to the tent.* AMANTHA *wanders to the car and sits on the bonnet.*

SHORTBOTHAM: Can't let the side down like that. Must keep a stiff upper lip, you know, and learn the discipline of the great out-doors. Breaking into tears just isn't cricket. (*She looks at* LILLY *and* CAMELIA.) Organization, that's what's needed here. (*She sees* AMANTHA.) Amantha! Come down from that disgusting car at once. You look like one of those cheap adverts in which you don't know if it's the car they're selling or the girl.

AMANTHA *slides off the bonnet and joins them.*

SHORTBOTHAM: Now, girls, let me see you put the tent up.

LILLY: We can't make it work, Miss.

SHORTBOTHAM: Can't you, dear? (*She inspects the tent, which is being held by* LILLY *and* CAMELIA.) How odd. Perhaps it does it from inside. Yes, that will be it. All get inside, girls, and we'll soon have it up.

They all crowd into the tent, which drapes over them, looking just as though it has been properly erected.

SHORTBOTHAM: Good, good. You see how teamwork helps? Never forget, girls. Pull together. Or is it push? I always forget. (*She joins the girls in the tent.*)

Enter the Gang, carrying a collection of car spares and repair equipment. PAUL *sees the tent and stops them all suddenly. They look at the tent a moment. Then* PAUL *waves them to follow him. He groups them round him down-stage of the car and away from the tent.* EDDIE *who is carrying a bucket, remains on the sky-line.*

PAUL: Invaders.

CHIPS: Bet they come from the town. Always having towny boys camping around here.

LOO: Not *more* boys. Oh, lor!

PIP: What can we do?

PAUL: If we don't get rid of them, we'll never get the car done up.

WALLY: Let's chuck bricks.

WILLY: Or some of these spares.

CHIPS: Or send Loo to nag at them. They'll soon go then.

PAUL: Don't be daft. Ask Eddie. (*He calls softly.*) Eddie!

EDDIE *walks down to them.*

PAUL: What do you think, Eddie?

EDDIE: You want rid of them?

PAUL: Yeah.

EDDIE: Don't know we're here, do they?

PAUL: No.

EDDIE: So best thing is to surprise them, isn't it?

CHIPS: Why?

EDDIE: Cos if we take them by surprise, they'll be easier to beat.

PAUL: Yeah. And once beaten, twice shy.

EDDIE: That's what I think. (*He walks back to the sky-line.*)

PAUL: I know. Put the stuff down. (*They put the equipment down.*) Follow me. When I shout now, jump on them. Chips, you stay here.

PAUL, SIMON, WILLY and WALLY stalk to the up-stage side of the tent. PAUL goes through the motions of indicating where each one is to fall.

PAUL: NOW!

They jump on to the tent. There are screams. The tent collapses. The girls scramble out. The boys are left rolling on the ground. MISS SHORTBOTHAM stands up. EDDIE finds himself immediately behind and above her. She is about to blow her whistle when EDDIE upturns his bucket of water over her. She is drenched; recovers and blows her whistle. Everything stops. The boys take in the situation at last and are horrified. PIP and LOO are hiding in the car, struggling with the giggles.

CHIPS: Oh, lor!

SHORTBOTHAM: And *what* do you think you are doing?

SIMON: Knew something like this would happen.

EDDIE begins to tiptoe away along the sky-line.

SHORTBOTHAM (*without turning*): Boy! Stand still!
  EDDIE *freezes.*

PAUL: We thought you were some boys invading our
  quarry and . . . well . . . we attacked.

SHORTBOTHAM: And what, young man, led you to
  believe you have sole posession of this quarry?

PAUL: Nothing, really. You see, our car is here and we
  didn't want anybody messing about with it.

SHORTBOTHAM (*disgusted almost beyond words*): You
  mean to say you play with THAT disgusting thing!
  (CHIPS *growls in indignation and turns his back on her.*)
  Girls, gather our things. We'll investigate this, young
  man. Attacking law-abiding campers in such a
  barbaric fashion. And littering the countryside with
  such . . . such . . . RUBBISH as that!

  CHIPS *almost explodes.*

PAUL: It isn't rubbish and we didn't litter it.

SHORTBOTHAM: SILENCE! You disgusting child.
  How dare you speak to me like that! I intend to
  report this incident to the police and to insist that the
  local refuse department remove that unseemly object
  – as much a danger to the public as it is unsightly to
  the eyes. Come, girls. We will find a less molested
  site and then see what can be done about these dis-
  graceful youths.

  Exit MISS SHORTBOTHAM *and her girls. As they go,*
  CHIPS *rushes up behind them in fury, shaking his fists
  above his head.*

PAUL: That's torn it.

  They all sit dejectedly. There is a long pause.

CHIPS: Expect we'll get twenty years for consultin' a
  lady.

WILLY: And there'll be swarms of police up here.

WALLY: Especially that Sherlock Holmes-type from the village. Caught me the other night without a light on my bike.

CHIPS: Then I'm glad I'm not you, Wally. They'll probably hang you for having other defences against you.

SIMON: It's all stupid anyhow. If we hadn't listened to that Luke, none of this would have happened.

PIP: It wasn't his fault, Simon. We should have found out who they were first.

CHIPS: Yes – Luke's all right. I like him. And it would have been smashing to have this car going.

SIMON: Wouldn't have been able to go anywhere in it.

CHIPS: So what! We could have run it up and down old Bones's field.

LOO: Some fun that would have been.

There is a long pause.

EDDIE: He's funny that Luke.

The others stir: it's unusual for EDDIE to say anything.

PAUL: How do you mean, Eddie?

EDDIE: He's funny. Odd. Doesn't add up. Well, I mean – all this about his dad and cars. And being on the road. And wanting to do up the car. Odd that is.

LOO: Even odder than most boys.

PIP: I know what you mean, Eddie. But I think he's all right really. I talked to him when you lot went off home.

PAUL: Wondered where you'd gone. What did he say?

PIP: Nothing much. He wouldn't talk about himself at first. He went all sullen when I asked him where he came from. And then I tried talking about cars and he told me all about his dad teaching him to drive.

CHIPS: There you are. See! He is all right.

LOO: Not all right at all. Saying he didn't want to talk about himself and then talking about his dad. Daft if you ask me. Bonkers.

PIP: There *was* something strange. He sort of went quiet all of a sudden, as though something was bothering him. Wouldn't say anything then. So I left him.

PAUL: Oh, well. All this has finished it. We might as well pack up.

SIMON: But if what Pip says is true, though, maybe we ought to do something about him.

LOO: Why?

SIMON: Well . . . he might need help or something.

PIP: I think we ought to try anyway. And it was being fun with the car.

PAUL: Come on, then. We'd better find Luke and tell him what's happened. One thing's sure. If that school woman goes to the police we'll have to get Luke out of the way. They'll get on to him straight away, looking like he does.

They gather the things they brought with them.

PAUL: Simon, you stay here in case Luke comes while we're looking.

Exit all but SIMON, *who sits on the car bonnet, his chin in his hands.* PAUL's *call 'Luke' can be heard in the distance. The afternoon is fading to evening.* MRS LOVE-JOY *enters along the sky-line. She is hesitant. Finally she comes into the quarry and approaches* SIMON *from behind, unheard. She looks just as she did in the scene with the* MAGISTRATE, *and carries her shopping bag.*

MRS LOVEJOY: You're Simon, aren't you?

    SIMON *starts, and is about to make off.*

MRS LOVEJOY: Don't run away. Please. It's all right. I won't bite.

    SIMON *relaxes.*

SIMON: What do you want?

MRS LOVEJOY: Just wanted to talk to you for a minute.

SIMON: Why? And how do you know who I am? I don't know you.

MRS LOVEJOY: My name's Mrs Lovejoy. I overheard what you were all saying just now, and I heard the tall one call you Simon.

SIMON: What do you want to talk about then?

MRS LOVEJOY: Luke.

SIMON: Oh, him!

MRS LOVEJOY: I know he can be difficult. But he's a good lad at heart.

SIMON: How do you know? You his mother?

MRS LOVEJOY: Not his mother quite. His foster-mother.

SIMON (*taken aback*): His foster-mother!

MRS LOVEJOY: That's right, dear. I look after him.

SIMON: But Luke says he has parents. You know – proper parents.

MRS LOVEJOY: He might have said that, Simon. But he hasn't. Not any more. He's lived with me for over a year. Least, he has for the time when he wasn't on the run.

SIMON: You mean he runs away?

MRS LOVEJOY: 'Fraid so, dear. That's the trouble now.

SIMON: We thought there was something up with him.

MRS LOVEJOY: He's always running off. Can't get

settled. I got him nicely settled after the court give him to me, and he run off and pinched five pounds.

SIMON: Five pounds!

MRS LOVEJOY: For food and stuff, to keep him going, you see. Then I got him back and settled at school and they told him he had to leave and get a job and he was up and off again.

SIMON: Didn't he want a job?

MRS LOVEJOY: Wasn't so much that he didn't want a job – he just couldn't face it. So he ran away. When they caught him the magistrate said that if he run off again he'd be sent to a Borstal school.

SIMON: And you mean he has? He's run off again?

MRS LOVEJOY: That's it, Simon. He's run off again.

SIMON: He's for it then.

MRS LOVEJOY: That's what I thought. But I thought to myself, Nora, I thought, you can't sit back and let this boy of yours be shut up in one of them awful places. No, I thought, you've got to do better than that.

SIMON: But what can you do? He *has* run off. And the magistrate will have to send him to Borstal when they catch Luke.

MRS LOVEJOY: That's just the point, dear. When he run off this time, I didn't tell a soul. I off after him. Took a risk. Give him his head, Nora, I said to myself. Let him have a good run for his money. Soon enough he'll come up against something he *can't* run away from, and he'll have to face it. So I trailed him. For five days I've trailed him. And it hasn't been easy. Not for him nor for me. But when I saw and heard what happened today, I thought, Nora, I thought, this is it. Without knowing it these youngsters will fetch him to his senses.

SIMON: How? We weren't doing anything special, were we?

MRS LOVEJOY: He's never had any friends, you see. And that's what he needs most – folk of his own age who just treat him like one of themselves. But now, after that business with that schoolmistress. Well . . . !

SIMON: We won't be able to help him any more.

MRS LOVEJOY (*hesitant*): So what I thought I'd ask you, Simon, though I know it would be hard for you . . . well . . . would you keep an eye on Luke? Just for a day or two? Not so's anybody would notice, like, and without him realizing, but just to keep things going on as they have.

SIMON: I could try, Mrs Lovejoy. But I don't know if I could do much. And if the police come and all that . . .

    EDDIE *has wandered on to the sky-line. He is unseen by* SIMON *and* MRS LOVEJOY. *At the word 'Police', he perks up and listens a moment before going silently behind an outcrop of rock, where he is hidden from view.*

MRS LOVEJOY: Now don't you worry. I'll find out what happens and watch for the police and let you know when they are coming. You let me know when you think Luke is ready to be picked up. How about that?

SIMON: Sounds a bit risky. But I'll try.

MRS LOVEJOY: Good lad. I knew you'd help me, soon as I laid eyes on you.

SIMON: What I don't understand, though, Mrs Lovejoy, is what caused it all in the first place.

MRS LOVEJOY: Can't tell you that now, Simon. Your friends will be back in a minute. But I will one day. I'll slip off now. Good luck, Simon.

SIMON: I'll probably need it.

Exit MRS LOVEJOY. *The light has faded to evening.* SIMON *turns and sits looking up-stage. The lights fade further until only the front of stage is lit. (The scene may be played in front of a curtain, if preferred.) A* POLICEMAN *enters, pushing or carrying a small table and chair. He sits.* MISS SHORTBOTHAM *and girls enter, possibly through the auditorium. She has changed and her wet clothes are carried on a line strung between two poles, held by* PRUNELLA *and* LILLY. *They stop in front of the* POLICEMAN, *who is hidden behind the clothes.*

SHORTBOTHAM: Good evening, Officer.

The POLICEMAN *stands behind the clothes, pulls the line down and looks over the top.*

POLICEMAN: Good evening, Miss.

SHORTBOTHAM: I wish to report a serious incident.

POLICEMAN: Yes, Miss. If you will just remove the er . . .

SHORTBOTHAM: Of course. How stupid. Girls, move away from the desk at once.

The girls stand aside. The POLICEMAN *sits and makes careful preparations for writing.*

POLICEMAN: Now, Miss. Your name, please.

SHORTBOTHAM: Miss Celia Shortbotham.

The POLICEMAN *looks stunned for a moment, then cranes his neck over the desk and peers at* SHORTBOTHAM's *lower half. He raises his eyebrows, licks his pencil and returns to his notebook.*

POLICEMAN (*writing*): Short-bottom.

SHORTBOTHAM:. It's spelt B-O-T-H-A-M.

POLICEMAN: Botham. (*He pronounces the 'th'.*) Now, Miss. Where did the incident take place?

SHORTBOTHAM: In the quarry, just an hour ago today. My girls were very upset.

POLICEMAN: Oh – the girls were there too?

SHORTBOTHAM: All the time. They saw everything, I'm sorry to say.

POLICEMAN: Well, now. This is very serious, Miss.

SHORTBOTHAM: I'm glad you take such a view of it, Officer. That such things can go on in a civilized community is quite outrageous.

POLICEMAN: Quite, Miss. Could I ask what happened?

SHORTBOTHAM: It's quite simple. We were preparing the tents for the night – we're on holiday, you know. I'm taking some of my girls to sample the life of the great out-doors and to study the local wild life on the way.

POLICEMAN (*glancing at the clothes*): Seems you found the wild life, anyway, Miss.

SHORTBOTHAM: We had erected the first tent and I had taken the girls inside to teach them a few tips about camp routine, when suddenly we were attacked by a vicious gang of hoodlums.

The POLICEMAN *jumps and whips out his truncheon.*

POLICEMAN: Hoodlums! What did they do, Miss?

SHORTBOTHAM: I hardly dare relate it all to you, Officer. (*She leans towards him confidentially.*) They tore down the tent about our heads and finished a fierce attack on us by drenching me in a disgusting liquid. As you see, my clothes are not yet dry.

POLICEMAN: Dreadful. How many were there?

SHORTBOTHAM: At *least* fifteen. There may have been more – hiding in the undergrowth, you know. And great frightening brutes they were too.

POLICEMAN: Could you describe them to me?

SHORTBOTHAM: It is all a horrible daze in my mind, Officer.

CAMELIA: I can remember one, Miss Shortbotham. He was little and kept making faces.

POLICEMAN: Little and making faces! (*Understanding begins to dawn.*) And was one tall and thin?

AMANTHA: Yes.

POLICEMAN: And were there a couple of girls?

AMANTHA: Yes.

POLICEMAN: And a pair of lads that is always together?

AMANTHA: Yes.

POLICEMAN: And maybe two other lads as well?

AMANTHA: Yes, yes.

CAMELIA: You've got it, Constable.

POLICEMAN (*relaxing and putting down his truncheon*): You needn't worry yourself, Miss. Them's the village kids. Meant no harm I don't expect.

SHORTBOTHAM: But . . .

POLICEMAN: Don't you mind them. They're always playing about up there. Know them all.

SHORTBOTHAM: Do you mean to say, Officer, that you won't investigate this matter after all?

POLICEMAN: I'll have a word with them, Miss, just to show I have my eye on them. But I shouldn't worry about it any more. You leave it to me. Hoodlums indeed!

(*He exits, shaking his head and chuckling to himself.*)

SHORTBOTHAM: Girls. To the Council Offices. We'll

see about this ourselves as the police here seem quite incapable.

A procession forms and they march round the stage. As they pass the table, the CLERK *enters and sits on it. She is young, very modern, brash, and busy manicuring her nails. As the school party approaches,* SHORTBOTHAM, *still furious, storms at the table. The* CLERK *is quite uninterested.*

SHORTBOTHAM: Young woman, I wish to have some scrap-metal removed.

CLERK: Yeah? What sort?

SHORTBOTHAM: A disgusting piece of automobile that is littering a public place.

CLERK: Put it in your dustbin and it'll be collected next time the van comes.

SHORTBOTHAM: I haven't got a dustbin and . . .

CLERK: Not having a dustbin is agin the council regulations. You'll be had up for ten quid if the boss finds out.

SHORTBOTHAM: Don't be silly, girl. I don't live here...

CLERK: Non-residents can't make use of the local services. Sorry.

SHORTBOTHAM: This is not *my* rubbish. It is a car which is abandoned and is littering a public way. It ought to be removed for the public safety.

CLERK: Why didn't you say that in the first place then, ducks. That's not my department. That's old Flutterbody's pigeon. (*She calls.*) Flutterbody! A customer.

Enter MISS FLUTTERBODY. *She is middle-aged, has a servile, patronizing manner, and lives up to her name.*

FLUTTERBODY: Good evening, Madam. I'm salvage.

SHORTBOTHAM: I beg your pardon?

CLERK: Yeah. They collected her years ago.

FLUTTERBODY: You have a request?

CLERK: She wants removing.

FLUTTERBODY: Now if I can just find my pad. Oh, dear, where is it?

The CLERK picks the pad from the desk and hands it to her. It is done without looking, like a daily routine.

FLUTTERBODY: Thank you, dear. Now where did I put my pencil?

The CLERK reaches out and takes the pencil from FLUTTERBODY's hair.

FLUTTERBODY: Thank you, dear. Now, Madam. Your name?

SHORTBOTHAM: Miss Celia Shortbotham. Spelt B-O-T-H-A-M.

FLUTTERBODY: Of course. Now. What is your trouble, Madam?

SHORTBOTHAM: I wish to have an abandoned car removed.

MISS FLUTTERBODY: Oh, I'm sorry, Madam. The council cannot undertake private work of that sort. You'll have to engage a garage company, I'm afraid.

SHORTBOTHAM: The machine is not mine, Miss Flutterbody. It has been parked by someone else and is obscuring a public way.

FLUTTERBODY: I see. How inconsiderate of someone to park a car in a public place. Then in that case, yes, of course. You *have* come to the right place. Yes. Salvage. That *would* be salvage. Yes. Yes. Indeed, yes.

CLERK: Glad you agree, Flutterbody, old girl.

FLUTTERBODY: You don't think that someone has just parked it there while they've gone shopping, do you?

SHORTBOTHAM: I really don't think so. It's in the quarry, you see.

FLUTTERBODY: Oh, well, in that case. I'll have it removed as soon as possible tomorrow, Miss Shortbotham. How exciting to have such an unusual request. It's usually only dustbins we've forgotten, you know!

BLACKOUT.

A pause. When the lights come up, it is twilight. SIMON *is where he was before the last scene. Noise of the gang returning.* LUKE *and* EARL *are with them.* PIP *carries a bag,* PAUL *a storm lantern. They are excited and race up to* SIMON.

PAUL: There's Simon.

CHIPS: We found Luke, Simon.

PAUL: With a friend who has some tremendous ideas for dealing with those girls. He's called Mr Earl.

SIMON: Hello, Mr Earl.

EARL: Good evening, my boy.

PAUL: He's got some terrific ideas.

CHIPS: Even Loo likes them.

LOO: Didn't say that.

CHIPS: Did!

PAUL: It was Pip's idea. Least the one about Luke was, wasn't it, Pip? Let's light the lantern and tell Simon, Pip.

PAUL *goes behind the car and lights the lantern.*

LUKE: It'll never work.

EARL: It will, my boy. A fine plan. I'm looking forward to a great deal of the fun myself.

CHIPS: So am us!

PAUL: Tell him, Pip.

PIP: I thought, Simon, that that schoolmistress is just the sort to tell the police and the council and do what she said. And we can't have that.

WILLY: Why should she spoil our fun?

CHIPS: Old balloon!

WALLY: Sh, Chips.

PIP: So I thought, first thing tomorrow we must get Luke looking normal. They'd pick on him straight-away, him looking so scruffy. Give him a good clean and a fresh set of clothes – some of Loo's brother's because he's just Luke's size. (*She turns on* LUKE.) And a hair cut.

LUKE: A hair cut! You didn't say that before.

PIP: I was saving it until now. You wouldn't have stood for it before.

The others are rubbing their hands in glee and anticipation.

LUKE: Won't stand for it now.

EARL: Now, Luke my boy. All in a good cause, you know. I shall be joining you in this business tomorrow. And I have a great deal more to lose than you. (*He strokes his beard.*)

LUKE: It isn't necessary.

PIP: You can't look all clean and tidy and normal with a mop like that. It's got to come off. And as a matter of fact I've got the things to do it now. (*She takes scissors and comb out of her bag.*)

LUKE (*backing away*): No . . . Not now . . . later!

He yells, and runs to escape. The others chase. He is caught, swung round, and sat on PAUL's *knee. The others gather round, blocking him from the audience.*

SIMON *stands on the car bonnet, holding the lantern over them.*

SIMON: Come on, Luke. It's for your own good. It's a great idea.

PIP (*clipping away with the scissors*): Quite right, Simon. I knew you'd agree.

SIMON: What about that big bit by his ear.

CHIPS: Have his ear!

There are shouts and hoots while the operation goes on.

PIP: There we are. Just a touch of the comb here and here. And . . . (*She stands away.*) Part one of the new Luke ready.

They scramble away. LUKE *falls from* PAUL's *knee. They all watch silently as he stands up. His back is to the audience. Once on his feet he turns slowly. The gang hoot with laughter and shout comments.*

LUKE: Crikey, I feel half naked.

EARL: That, old fellow, is nothing to what you'll feel like tomorrow when your young friends have completed the operation.

LOO: You even look vaguely handsome now.

PIP (*bringing her bag to the middle of the stage*): And as a reward I've brought some cakes mum made today. She doesn't know they're gone yet. But we'll cross that bridge when we come to it.

Shouts. They gather round, grabbing food. EARL *coughs for attention.*

EARL: As you know, I called in at a local hostelry on our way back tonight. (*They jeer.*) You all, I'm sure, thought I was indulging in a little . . . weakness. (*More jeers.*) In truth, however, I was purchasing with the last of my ill-gotten gains, a few gifts to add to our

little repast. (*He produces from pockets all over him,
bottles of squash and lemonade. The gang cheer at this
final delight, grab a bottle and go off to various parts of the
quarry, where they sit and guzzle.* EARL *goes round
taking off tops from bottles. As he does so he sings:*)

EARL: Oh all the money that e're I spent:
  I spent it in good company.
  And all the harm that e're I've done,
  Alas it was to none but me.
  And all I've done for want of wit
  To memory now I can't recall.
  So fill to me, the parting glass:
  Good night, and joy be with you all.

  Oh all the comrades that e're I had
  Are sorry for my going away.
  And all the sweethearts that e're I had
  Would wish me one more day to stay.
  But since it comes unto my lot
  That I should rise and you should not;
  I'll gently rise and I'll softly call –
  Good night, and joy be with you all.

*He climbs into the car, yawns and stretches. The others
have settled down, content and sleepy.*
EARL: It's bed for this dear old vehicle and me, my
friends. Good night to you. (*He lies down in the back
seat. His feet come over the car body on the down-stage
side. He has taken off his boots. His toes are sticking
through great holes in his socks. The toes wiggle.*
EARL: God rest.
  The others stir, stand, rub crumbs from themselves and

begin to leave, calling 'good night' to EARL. PAUL *takes the lantern. As it goes the stage is left in moonlight, a shaft of which glances on the car.* PIP *has hung back. She comes forward and gathers the bag and food remains as the last of the gang go.* LUKE *is moving towards the car as she finishes collecting the things. An owl hoots.*

PIP: It's been fun today, Luke.

LUKE: Yes, great. I'm . . . glad I met you lot.

PIP: And I'm glad we met you.

The owl hoots again. EARL *snores loudly.* PIP *and* LUKE *laugh.*

PIP: He's happy anyhow.

LUKE: Yeah. The good sleep deep.

PIP: How odd you should say that. My mum says it too!

LUKE: Does she? (*He turns away so that he is facing the car, his smile gone.*) I learned it from mine.

The theme is heard, softly. It plays through until the curtain.

PIP (*moving towards the sky-line*): Well then. Sleep well.

LUKE: I'll try.

PIP: Tomorrow will be a busy day.

LUKE (*climbing into the front seat of the car*): Yeah. See you.

PIP: Good night, Luke. See you tomorrow.

LUKE: Hope so.

Exit PIP. LUKE *is settled out of sight in the car.* EDDIE *comes from the projection of rock where he has been hidden. He walks slowly to the car and looks at* LUKE *for a moment. He exits, following* PIP.

CURTAIN

ACT TWO

The music: brighter and more lively.
The quarry, noon the next day. The car is transformed. It shines in a new coat of paint, very blotchily applied, as though slapped on hurriedly. Some of the gang are just finishing off the work. LOO is putting the last tacks into a patch on the old collapsed roof canvas. LUKE is under the car at the front, his legs sticking out. He is doing something to the front axle. PAUL is working at a wheel. WILLY and WALLY, paint brushes in hands, are walking round the car, touching the new paint tentatively with their finger-ends. CHIPS is sitting on the back of the driving-seat, his feet on the driving-wheel.

CHIPS: I aren't half hungry. We've been at it all morning.
PAUL: Not long now, Chips. We've nearly finished.
WILLY: This paint's nearly dry.
WALLY: You come and see, Paul. Nearly dry already.
PAUL: Quick-drying paint. Got it from my dad.
CHIPS: He gave you that! Doesn't sound like him. It's expensive, that stuff.
PAUL: It's his all right. And I got it from him. He doesn't know I've got it, that's all.

He finishes with the wheel, gets up and stands back. The others join him, appraising their handiwork.

CHIPS: That's smart, Paul.

PAUL: Not so bad. Paint's run a bit.

WALLY: Had to put it on so quick.

WILLY: Looks great, though. I'm dying to see what happens if them men come.

PAUL: They'll come. Eddie saw that school woman going into the council office, didn't he?

CHIPS: Yeah, he did. They'll come all right. Meddlin' lot.

LOO: And fancy being taught by that school woman!

CHIPS: Ugh! (*He pretends to be sick.*)

PAUL: Mr Earl will be ready if they do come, though.

LOO: Be a right laugh if he pulls it off.

PAUL: Won't half. Time we went off home. Where's Eddie and Simon?

CHIPS: Dunno. Simon went off somewhere ages ago. And Eddie went just after him.

WILLY: Skiving.

WALLY: Yeah. Skiving. Leaving us to do the work.

CHIPS: Simon probably had to help his mum. Always making him help, she is.

PAUL: They'll turn up. (*He goes to* LUKE *and bends to see what he's doing.*) You nearly finished, Luke?

LUKE: Yeah. Won't be long. It's the steering. Want to be sure it's safe.

PAUL: It's time we went for dinner.

LUKE: You go. I'll not be long and there's nothing more we can do.

PAUL: Pip's gone to get you some clothes to change into. And I expect she'll bring you some eats. Shouldn't be long now.

LUKE: O.K.

PAUL: See you then.

LUKE: Yeah.

PAUL: Come on, you lot.

Exit the gang, leaving LUKE *under the car. The music is heard. There is a pause, then* PIP *enters along the skyline. She carries a bag. She comes into the quarry and stands up-stage of* LUKE'*s feet. She peers down, trying to see what he's doing, and smiles at his grunts. Suddenly* LUKE *shouts with pain and wriggles out. He has cut his arm. He gets up, holding the wounded arm carefully.* PIP *has kept behind him so that he does not know she is there.*

PIP: Let me help. Have you hurt yourself?

LUKE (*turning and seeing her*): Oh, hello. Didn't know you were there. Not much. Just cut it on a bit of metal.

PIP inspects the wound, opens her bag, takes out a handkerchief or a piece of cloth.

PIP: Sit up there.

LUKE sits on the car bonnet. PIP *begins to doctor the wound.*

PIP: It's not too bad. Soon have it O.K. Men always shout before they're hurt. I've brought you some dinner.

LUKE: Thanks. (*He winces.*) Ow!

PIP: Stop bellowing. Anyone would think you were dying.

LUKE: Girls are hard.

PIP: Nonsense. I've got your clothes too.

LUKE: Do I *have* to change?

PIP: Of course. Can't keep you with us if you don't look normal like the rest of us. Somebody is bound to ask questions if the council men do come. And anyway, I've told my mum I've a friend I want to bring home, so you'd better look right!

LUKE: Bossy as well as hard, girls are.

PIP: Why? Don't you want to come?

LUKE: Yes. Wouldn't mind. You're O.K., you lot.

PIP (*finishing the dressing*): Thanks, kind sir! Anyway, you'll have to change. You smell as you are.

LUKE: Huh! (*He laughs. An idea occurs to him. He reseats himself primly on the bonnet and gives* PIP *a huge, toothy smile. He imitates a TV advert voice*): Even your best friends won't tell you. Beware! You can have it without knowing. (*He holds out his arms languidly, sniffs under his arm-pits, blows out and pulls a disgusted face.*) Don't be rank, rancid or tainted; musty, fusty or frousty. (*He gives the toothy grin.*) Use 'Honesty' – the soap that blows away the B.O. in big bouncy bubbles. Don't just be clean (*he smells under his arms again, but this time returns an exotic look*), smell clean, with fragrant 'Honesty'.

PIP (*laughing*): I've thought of that too.

LUKE: Oh, no!

PIP (*taking soap and a towel from her bag*): Here's some soap, and a towel. There's a pool over there. You can clean up in a minute.

LUKE: Is there anything you haven't thought of?

PIP: Yes – a toothbrush. So you'll have to finish off with this apple. (*She takes an apple from her bag.*)

LUKE (*taking the apple and getting down from the bonnet*): Thanks. And thanks for doing up my arm.

PIP: That's all right. (*A pause.* LUKE *is gnawing the apple.*) You know I really am surprised your mum lets you roam about like you do. Ours wouldn't let us.

LUKE *is arrested as he is about to take a bite of the apple. His hand drops to his side. He breathes in deeply.*

LUKE (*with difficulty*): I haven't got a mother.

    PIP *is taken aback.*

PIP: Oh . . . I'm sorry, Luke . . . I didn't know.

LUKE: It's O.K. Don't worry. It's over. Nothing to bother about. (*He gets into the car.*) Where's them clothes?

PIP: But, Luke . . . if you've no mother then . . .

LUKE: Girls are nosy too! Ask no questions and you'll get no lies. One day you'll know maybe. I'll tell you. but not yet. It's all over. See?

PIP: If it was all over you wouldn't be here, would you?

LUKE (*uncertain*): How d'you mean?

PIP: Stands to reason. If it was all over, you'd be settled somewhere. You should be in school or at work and you're not.

LUKE: Proper old Sherlock Holmes, ain't you!

PIP: That's what Eddie said, and he was right.

LUKE: Been talking about me, have you?

PIP: I told you last night it was odd finding you here like we did. We're bound to wonder, aren't we? Luke . . . it's not that I'm nosy or anything . . . just, it would be nice to know about you. We all like you.

LUKE: I know. It's been good these last two days. At first I liked it up here cos it was out of the way and nobody came. I'd been on the road nearly five days then, and I was just beginning to feel like going back.

PIP: Back where, Luke?

LUKE: Back to the woman who looks after me. Lovejoy her name is. Mrs Lovejoy. Her husband's dead and they didn't have any kids. She got me after . . . after mum and dad went.

PIP: Do you like her?

LUKE: Mrs Lovejoy? She's O.K. She always done her best for me. She's kind and all that, you know. I'm fond of her really. But . . . somehow . . . it isn't enough. I get restless. Once before I ran off. Tramped about for eight days that time. Copper in Huddersfield picked me up. Ever been to Huddersfield?

PIP: No.

LUKE: Then don't. Not even if you want to go somewhere no one will think of looking! Anyhow, yesterday I was in half a mind to go back and just hope that she hadn't asked the coppers to look for me again – I'd really get it this time, if she did.

PIP: But you didn't.

LUKE: No. You lot came. And it's been different since. Like a different world, where it didn't matter who I was or what had happened to me. You all just took me as I am. (*He pauses. They look at each other. Then with a great breath, he makes himself active again.*) As I say, it's been great with you lot – and now I'm going to change ready for the rest of the fun. (*He gets out of the car, takes the bag and is about to exit, when he stops and turns back slowly, a wry smile on his face.*) Here! No looking, mind!

PIP (*laughing*): I won't. I promise. Anyway – doubt if you're any different from our Paul.

LUKE: No. Except Paul's your brother, isn't he?

PIP (*more cautiously*): Yes, he is.

LUKE: And that makes a difference, don't it?

PIP: Yes, I suppose it does.

LUKE: Yeah! Well . . . see you!

He turns to go off. Before he is gone, SIMON *rushes in, breathless.*

SIMON: Luke! Pip! They're coming. The council men. They'll be here any minute.

PIP: How do you know?

SIMON: I've been watching for them, and I saw them setting off from the council yard so I rushed up to warn you. I caught Chips on the way, and he's going to tell Paul and Mr Earl.

LUKE: Then I'm off to change somewhere else. Too late to do it here now.

PIP (*rushing to him and grabbing his hand*): Come with me. I know a good place farther down.

> LUKE *and* PIP *exit hurriedly.*

SIMON (*shouting as they go*): For Heaven's sake hurry! They'll be here in a minute. (*He looks off-stage.*) Oh, lor! They're here!

> SIMON *jumps into the quarry. Makes for the car. Decides against it as a place to hide. Makes for the outcrop where* EDDIE *hid. Decides against that. Finally, he runs off after* PIP *and* LUKE. EDDIE *appears from the direction* SIMON *came from. He is not at all agitated. He calmly follows* SIMON, *whom he is obviously trailing.*

> *Enter the* FOREMAN *and his three* COUNCIL MEN. *They are panting and grunting after the exertion of the climb.* MAN 1 *carries a green and a red flag. At present the green is raised. When they stop, he raises the red one.* MAN 2 *is small, and all but lost in his overall and coloured roadman's waistcoat.* MAN 3 *is huge and carries a spade, as well as an old army water bottle, which is strapped over his shoulders.*

> *They stop at the top of the quarry sky-line, exhausted. They gaze into the quarry, at the car.*

FOREMAN: There she is, men.

MEN: Ah! There she be.

The MEN *descend heavily. The* FOREMAN *begins the descent when something occurs to him. He stops, puts a whistle into his mouth and blows. The* MEN *freeze.*

FOREMAN: Brovers!

The MEN *turn and group near him.*

FOREMAN (*as though addressing a large public meeting*): Brovers, the Rules, Regulations and Articles governin' our Union. (*He produces a tattered book.*) A copy of which doc-u-ment I 'appen to 'ave 'ere for per-usual – states, in chapter 53, paragraph 5, subsection 3, part 1 – I quote, Brovers – 'No member of the Union can be employed in heavy manual labour of any kind that may adversely affect his well-being for any period of not less than three minutes after ascending a hill, incline, slope or ladder for fifty feet or more.' I unquote the quote.

MAN 3 *is puzzled.* MAN 2 *climbs on to the blade of* MAN 3*'s shovel, and bellows into his ear:*

MAN 2: That do mean we mustn't get tired.

MAN 3: Oh, ah?

MAN 2 *returns to his place.*

FOREMAN: This bank what we 'ave just appended, Brovers, is all of fifty feet or more. I therefore call on you, Brovers, to operate the fifty-foot rule and to insist on taking a hard-earned rest.

MAN 1: Does this mean, Brover, that what we have to do is nothing?

FOREMAN: Indubitably, Brover.

The FOREMAN *takes out a huge alarm clock, consults it and blows his whistle. The* MEN *find places to sit down.* MAN 2 *sits on the ground, leaning against the car radiator.*

MAN 1 *is holding up his red flag.* MAN 3 *drinks messily from his bottle. The* FOREMAN, *clock held out, stomps over to the car and eyes it critically. He puts his clock away, takes out his rule book, consults it, puts it away, takes out his clock again, prepares his whistle and blows. The* MEN *struggle to their feet.*

FOREMAN: Brovers. The Rules, Regulations and Articles governin' our union, states quite caste-phorically – I quote, Brovers – 'Any dangerous or 'armful item of disposable material which might crush, maim, impale or unduly tire the removal oper-a-tives, shall not be removed, dismantelled or disposed of without first being inspected by the proper authorities and an extra allowance of danger money being made.' I unquote, Brovers.

MAN 2 (*climbing* MAN 3's *spade again*): That do mean we can't lift it.

MAN 3: Thank you, Brover.

FOREMAN: No danger money 'as been awarded in this case, Brovers. However, in the circus-stances, I will make han inspection on be'alf of the hemployers, and demand danger money when we return.

The MEN *begin to understand the* FOREMAN's *drift and grow enthusiastic.*

FOREMAN: In the event of that danger money not being impregnated forthwith, we shall call a three-day strike. (*The* MEN *grow even more agitated.*) That strike to cover a period that will hit the hemployers worst: the three days of the Peghampton Races. (*The* MEN *are about to explode with delight.*) And, incidentally Brovers, this will also make it possible for us to attend the race meeting.

The MEN *whoop with joy, jump in the air, mime the riding of horses, and cheer.*

FOREMAN: All those in favour show.

MAN 1 *and* 2 *put up a hand.* MAN 3 *stands, unresponsive still grinning with pleasure at the last announcement.* MAN 2 *crosses to him and climbs the spade.*

MAN 2: That do mean put your hand up.

MAN 3: Oh! Thank you, Brover.

MAN 3 *raises his hand. It is the hand which holds the spade. The spade falls to the ground with* MAN 2 *on it. He screams. He pulls himself to his feet and raises his hand.*

FOREMAN: Carried unanimously. I will now make my officious inspection.

He walks to the front of the car. The MEN *group behind him. He bends to look under the car. The* MEN *bend with him.*

Enter EARL. *He has been dressed in a smart suit. His beard has been clipped and his hair tidied. He looks the epitome of the salesman type.*

EARL: Gentlemen! How fortunate you are that we have met.

The FOREMAN *and* MEN *rise, open-mouthed.*

EARL: I have just this moment returned from my lunch and here I find you wishing to inspect this bargain automobile.

FOREMAN (*recovering and wishing to re-establish himself.*) Just one minute. If I could just make a statement.

EARL: Do, sir, do.

FOREMAN: I think I should make it clear that our presence here in no way maligns us with your views.

EARL: Of course not. Heavens, no. (*He eyes the* FOREMAN.) Have you a car, sir?

The FOREMAN *looks uncomfortable. The* MEN *crowd to hear his answer.*

FOREMAN: No. As a matter of fact, I 'aven't.

EARL (*scandalized*): You haven't a . . . ! My dear sir! A man in your position!

FOREMAN: All the fault of the indiscriminate procrastination of the hemployers.

EARL: Then, sir, you have come to the right place to correct that regrettable state of affairs. Here I have in remarkable condition a vintage car of superb lines and preservation.

FOREMAN: Vintage?

EARL: All the rage just now, sir. May I ask you to try the driving-seat. (*He manhandles the* FOREMAN *into the seat.*) Can't you feel the ancient comfort of the upholstery. That bumpy surface of the seat which speaks of everlasting springs and seasoned leather?

The FOREMAN *is bouncing up and down. The* MEN *are poking about.*

FOREMAN: Bit hard on the old buttocks though, isn't it?

EARL: Ah! But what would you prefer? That – or the inferior life of this modern rubbish that bursts after one good afternoon's bouncing? This car is made to last. Look at its solid worth. No mass-produced slickness about this vehicle.

The MEN *are trying this and that. A headlamp comes off in* MAN 2's *hands.*

EARL (*taking the lamp and replacing it*): Adjustable headlamps, sir. Thank you for pointing it out.

MAN 3: What about the engine, then?

EARL: The engine, sir? As new. You'll not have seen a

better. In fact, I'm so confident about it . . . that I'm not going to bother showing it to you. Have you noticed the upholstery?

FOREMAN: Bit tatty, isn't it?

EARL: I'm glad you mentioned that, sir. The new craze in the old car class. Called – The Patched Look. Upholstery deliberately made to look patchy and repaired. Makes your old car look older still. Goes with the blotchy paintwork. All part of the design at no extra cost.

MAN 1: What about the cost then?

EARL: That, sir, is a very shrewd question. Most people just pass over that one. But I see I have in you a man who knows his business.

MAN 1: Well . . . I'm not exactly easy to take for a ride.

    EARL *roars with laughter.*

EARL: Excellent pun, sir. Very funny.

    The MEN *stand blankly. The* FOREMAN *gets out of the car.*

FOREMAN: Yes, what about the price?

EARL: If I told you the price, sir, you would be quite astounded. You just would not believe that any firm could bring themselves to sell such a machine at such a price. You may have a trial period with this superb car, a trial period lasting one week. If at the end of that time you are satisfied and would like to purchase the car, we will reveal the price. And for that privilege we ask only a five pound down payment. Could anything be more generous or handsomely honest?

MAN 2: You just can't refuse, Howard.

FOREMAN: Well, I don't know. It's quite a sum just to try an old car.

MAN 2: You have a try, Howard.

FOREMAN: Must say, it sounds very hattractive. (*He ponders.*) Very well. (*He takes a wallet from his pocket and produces five pounds.*) There's five pounds on the nail. I'll be up tomorrow to collect the car.

EARL: Thank you, sir. I hope you won't be disappointed. The car will be waiting!

The MEN *each shake the* FOREMAN'S *hand. Then he looks at his clock. He blows his whistle. The* MEN *come to order.*

FOREMAN: Brovers. It's five minutes to five o'clock. In accordance with Union Regulations we must claim overtime for the return journey.

The MEN *agree cheerfully. The* FOREMAN *blows his whistle and the* MEN *storm out,* MAN 3 *celebrating by taking another messy drink as he goes. The* FOREMAN *shakes hands with* EARL *and exits behind the* MEN.

The gang enter from the opposite side of the stage. They are bursting with glee and when the MEN *are well clear, cheer* EARL, *and laugh.*

EARL: It was nothing, nothing at all.

CHIPS: Five pounds. Phew! That's . . . 300 ice-creams.

LOO: A fool and his money are soon parted.

EARL: True, true. We did, as they would have said, take them for a ride.

They all laugh. The laugh changes to a jeer as enter LUKE *and* PIP. LUKE *has been changed into his new clothes. He is smart, his hair neatly combed, and his face cleaned up. He walks stiffly, not liking the clothes at all.*

CHIPS: Crickey, Luke, you haven't half changed.

LUKE: Feels all prickly and stiff.

PIP: That's because they're clean. Shows how long

you've been in that cocoon of dirt. (*To the others.*)
Honestly, you should see the water in the spinney pool
now. Black as indian ink.

They all laugh.

LUKE: All right for you lot. You didn't have to put up
with her – she even scrubbed my back with sea grass.
I'm red raw under this lot.

PAUL: Never mind, Luke. Mr Earl did it. He sold the
car to the council men. Five pounds!

LUKE: Great. What we going to do with the money?

EARL: Perhaps we ought to give it to some charity.

CHIPS: My mum says charity begins at home, so why
not start on us!

The gang yell their agreement and charge off with EARL
in tow. PIP *goes to follow but stops when she sees* LUKE
going to the car.

PIP: You coming?

LUKE (*turning to her*): They'll be back soon.

PIP *comes to him, looking him up and down approvingly.*

PIP: You do look nice in your new clothes and your
hair cut.

LUKE: Thanks.

They look at each other a moment, then LUKE *suddenly
bends towards her and kisses her on the cheek.* PIP *turns
away, startled.*

PIP: What was that for?

LUKE: Fun!

PIP: You shouldn't do things like that just for fun.

LUKE: Why not?

PIP: It means too much to do it for fun. To me, anyway.

LUKE: Me too.

PIP (*turning back to him*): Oh!

LUKE: Yes.

PIP: Then . . . what *did* it mean?

LUKE: That I like you, I suppose.

PIP: Thanks. (*Hesitantly.*) I like you too.

LUKE: Do you? That makes things even better then, doesn't it?

PIP: I suppose it does.

LUKE: You ever been kissed before?

PIP (*ironically*): Millions of times. Boys just queue up every day. Can't hold them off. How about you?

LUKE: It's just the same with me. Except it's girls that queue up for me, of course. Do you know, it's so bad I have to take holidays miles from anywhere just to get out of their way.

PIP: I know. Awful, isn't it! (*They laugh.* PIP *moves to the car and climbs into the passenger-seat.*) Wouldn't it be lovely if we could go for a ride?

LUKE (*acting the chauffeur*): And where would Madam wish to go?

PIP (*acting the great lady*): Now let me see . . . Of course. Young man: drive me to that place where the buildings are beautiful . . .

LUKE: Athens?

PIP: And the sun shines all day out of a clear sky . . .

LUKE: Madrid?

PIP: And there's theatres and gardens and famous places . . .

LUKE: London?

PIP: And the people are gay and friendly . . .

LUKE: I've got it, Madam, Paris.

PIP (*in broad Yorkshire*): Paris, luv? No – Huddersfield!
   LUKE'*s face reacts in disgust and he pretends to be sick over the side. They laugh.*

PIP: But really, I should like to go for a ride down a lovely country road, with the breeze blowing in my hair and the sun sparkling through the green leaves in the trees.

LUKE: Yeah, that is a good feeling.

PIP: And I should make you drive faster and faster, just to see the hedges go flashing by and feel the thrill of the speed and . . .

LUKE (*starting out of the car horrified*): No!

PIP (*rushing to him, puzzled at his reaction*): What's the matter, Luke? I was only imagining.

LUKE (*shouting at her*): Shut up, will you!
   PIP *turns away, hurt. There is a tense silence. Slowly,* LUKE *gets control of himself and turns to* PIP.

LUKE: I'm sorry, Pip.

PIP (*turning to face him. They are very close*): That's all right. (*She smiles and sighs.*) You are an old funny. (*She kisses him on the cheek, gently.*)

LUKE (*taking off a medallion that hangs about his neck*): I want you to have this.

PIP: What is it?

LUKE: A sort of keepsake. It's a Saint Christopher. (*He puts it round her neck.*)

PIP: Thanks, Luke. It's lovely. I'll wear it always.

LUKE: That's what I hoped. (*Brightly.*) Anyway, you go speeding round the place, you'll need it.
   Enter the gang. They are finishing ice-cream cornets. EARL *is not with them.*

PAUL: You should have come, you two. These ices are smart.

CHIPS: Bet you've been playing postman's knock in that car.

PIP: Don't be silly, Chips.

CHIPS: I wasn't silly. I went and had an ice-cream.

PAUL: Anyway, what with Mr Earl selling the car and Pip's work on you, Luke, all's well.

A pause.

EDDIE: It would be, if Simon hadn't told on us.

They all look with uncomprehending faces at EDDIE. PAUL *tenses.*

PAUL: Say that again, Eddie.

EDDIE: I said it would be all right if Simon hadn't told the police of us.

The mood changes. They turn with antagonistic looks towards SIMON. *He sits, speechless, eyeing them.* PAUL *moves towards him, glaring at him.*

PAUL: Grab him.

WILLY *and* WALLY *go to either side of* SIMON, *who is still sitting watching developments. Things hang in mid-air for a second. Then* SIMON *makes a dash.* WILLY *and* WALLY *spring at him and pull him down. He tries to rise but they chop him down again.* WILLY *and* WALLY *stand, dragging* SIMON *up by the arms. They throw him forward then swing him back against the quarry where they pin him with his arms held out.*

PAUL: Chips, take Simon's shoes.

CHIPS *backs away.*

CHIPS: No . . . I don't want to . . .

CHIPS *backs into* PIP *who holds him protectively.*

PIP: No, Paul. Let Simon speak first.

PAUL: Shut up, Pip. Chips.

Reluctantly CHIPS *crosses to* SIMON, *who has already worked his shoes off.* CHIPS *takes them, glances guiltily at* SIMON *and goes to the quarry sky-line where he sits dejectedly.*

PIP *rushes up to* PAUL.

PIP: Paul, you've got to let Simon tell us what he's done.

PAUL: None of us ever tells on the others. We've always had that rule.

PIP: But you don't know that he's done what Eddie says.

PAUL: Has Eddie ever lied? He never says anything he doesn't know is right, does he?

PIP: No – but everyone can be wrong once.

WILLY: Eddie ain't never wrong.

WALLY: Eddie knows everything.

WILLY: That's why we keep him in the gang.

WALLY: So there!

LUKE *has climbed into the car.*

PAUL: Look at Luke. Think how he feels after everything that's happened.

PIP: I don't care, Paul. You've got to hear both sides.

PAUL: How can you say that after everything we've done? Selling the car and doing up Luke so that if anybody comes they won't know him. Talk sense.

PIP: I am talking sense. There's no sense in going on what one person says just because they're usually right.

LOO: No good trying to tell boys anything, Pip. They always think they're right.

PIP: Well, I won't stand for it. If you do anything to

Simon without hearing both sides, I'll . . . (*She stops short.*)

PAUL: Well . . . go on. Tell on us. That's what you were going to say, wasn't it? Well, wasn't it?

PIP (*quietly but firmly*): No, Paul. I won't tell on you. But you won't be my brother any more. I wouldn't have you for a brother if you stooped that low.

PAUL: What's so low about thumping a traitor?

PIP: You'd be low, Paul, because you'd hurt somebody for doing something they thought was right. Or maybe not doing anything at all. You'd be low because you'd hit first and talked afterwards. You'd be low because a mob like you all are now is always low. (PAUL *turns away furiously, breathing hard.* PIP *goes on, gaining pace and conviction.*) How do you know he's a traitor? How do you know what he's done? Have you asked him? What did Eddie see? Have you asked *him* that?

PAUL (*furious and trying to hold his temper*): All right! All right! Have your own way. We'll hear both.

PIP *leaves him and turns away.*

PAUL: Go on, Eddie.

EDDIE *stalks up to* SIMON. *He takes his time, is unflustered, but when he speaks there is strong malice in his voice.*

EDDIE: I been watching Simon since last night. I came into the quarry while you lot were searching for Luke and he was here with a woman. He was talking all matey-like with her, and I heard her say she'd watch for the police coming if Simon would tell her when Luke was ready to be picked up. I watched him last night until you'd all gone and I followed him

again this morning. Ever since he came out of his
house I've followed him.

WILLY: What happened, Eddie?

EDDIE: He saw that woman again this morning. They
talked just before dinner, after we'd done up the car.

PAUL: What did they say?

EDDIE: I couldn't hear because they were on the road
just out of the village where there ain't no hedges for
cover and I could get near enough. But they were
heads together like two turtle-doves.

PIP: Do you know who the woman is, Eddie?

EDDIE: Never seen her before. Heard Simon call her
Mrs Lovejoy.

PIP (*quietly* to LUKE): Mrs Lovejoy! Would she?

  LUKE, *starting like a betrayed animal, shrugs.* PIP
  climbs into the car beside him.

PAUL: All right.

  EDDIE *goes up on to the quarry sky-line, where he
  stands dictatorially, watching.*

PAUL: Now, Simon.

  SIMON *hangs his head.*

PAUL: Haven't you anything to say? (SIMON *doesn't
move.*) But you must have. (*Pause.*) *Did* you talk to
this woman? Did you tell the police about Luke?
(PAUL *is growing angry. Finally he bursts away from*
SIMON.) What did you do it for? You feeble coward!
That's what you are. You've told on your own friends
and you haven't the guts to own up. (*He points at*
PIP.) She talks about being low. You've been going
behind our backs like a nasty little snake in the grass.
You've been pretending to be one of us just so you can
suck up to rotten adults and butter them up with tales

about what we've been doing, just so's they can catch up with Luke. You're a creep, you are. A coward and a creep. (*He pauses, breathing hard.*) And what's more, you don't know about being friends. (*He looks at the others, all sullenly watching.*) Is he guilty? (*No one answers.*) Wally. Is Simon guilty?

WALLY (*reluctantly*): Yes.

PAUL: Willy?

WILLY *nods.*

PAUL: Chips?

CHIPS: I dunno. He hasn't said anything, has he?

PAUL: If he hasn't said anything, that means he's done it.

CHIPS: I suppose so. But I wish he wasn't.

PAUL: Eddie?

EDDIE: Guilty. I seen him do it.

PAUL: All right then. (*Slowly and deliberately.*) I say Simon should be out of the gang for good. Does everyone say yes? (*There are murmurs of agreement, except from* EDDIE, *who gives a clear, Yes.*) Eddie. Fetch that tin of oil and the brush from the car.

EDDIE *crosses to the car, takes a tin of oil and a brush from the back seat, goes to* PAUL *and puts them in his outstretched hand.* PAUL *is glaring at* SIMON. EDDIE *then returns to the sky-line.*

PAUL: Willy. Wally. Take off Simon's shirt.

WILLY *and* WALLY *rip* SIMON's *shirt from his shoulders.*

PAUL: This is to show that Simon isn't in the gang any more.

PAUL *dips the brush carefully into the oil. Then he paces with deliberate steps up to* SIMON. *He raises the brush and slashes it across* SIMON'*s chest. He dips the brush and slashes it again. He is preparing for a third stroke when* LUKE *shouts:*

LUKE: Stop it! (*He rushes at* PAUL *and knocks the brush from his hand.*) Stop it! Leave him alone.

PAUL *and* LUKE *glare at each other a moment before* PAUL *gives way. He goes on to the sky-line and stands back to audience.* LUKE *pulls* WILLY *and* WALLY *from* SIMON. *They too get out of the way.* SIMON *rubs his arms, confronted by* LUKE.

LUKE (*quietly*): Was it Mrs Lovejoy?

SIMON *nods.*

LUKE: Was she putting the police on to me?

SIMON: No, Luke, honest. She was trying to keep them off.

LUKE: You mean she was protecting me?

SIMON: I suppose so.

LUKE: Why didn't you tell Paul that?

SIMON: Mrs Lovejoy didn't want them to know about you.

LUKE: And you was helping her?

SIMON: Yes.

LUKE: You mean she's been following me all this time and didn't stop me or tell anybody I'd gone off?

SIMON: Nobody but me, and she only told me so I could help when it looked like the police might be coming to see us about them girls. She says you had to have your head so she let you keep running.

LUKE: Why?

SIMON: Well . . . she thought you'd come back to her

sooner or later. Kept talking about getting something
out of your system and facing up to things. I didn't
understand.

LUKE: And you wouldn't even split to Paul.

SIMON: No.

LUKE (*almost to himself, coming forward and looking into
the audience*): She thought I'd get it out of my system.
Thought I'd face up to it.

The music is heard. And then the echoing voice of the
MAGISTRATE: '*You cannot go on running away. We
cannot allow it. You must learn to face things like a
man.*' *And* LUKE's *voice*: '*He couldn't understand it at
first, but when I told him he said, "Never run, boy".*' *The
lights are fading and will soon leave only the car picked out
in a spot.*

LUKE (*to himself*): Never run away. (*He turns to face the
others.*) I want to tell you lot something. (*They all
settle down on the sky-line, leaving the car empty.*) I'm not
just tramping about. I'm on the run. And I haven't any
parents like I told you I had. I haven't had for a year.
Exactly a year ago since the day I ran last week. We
did everything together, mum, dad and me. We
had a small house on the outskirts of town. I was an
only one. Dad was a skilled mechanic. Great with
engines he was. And we had this car that he kept like
it was a pedigree. Folks envied that car for miles
around. (*The music is heard softly.*) Every Sunday we
went for a drive. Sometimes we took all the meals for
the day and stopped at pubs and bought beer and
lemonade. And if it was hot and sunny, we'd picnic in a
field. One day last spring we were going to set off
early and visit one of them big country houses that

Lords let you look round. Mum got the picnic basket all ready.

The lights have faded now until the car alone is lit. MRS LAWSON *enters. She is middle-aged, brisk and trim. She is a firm but affectionate mother. She carries the picnic basket. As she speaks the music fades away.*

MAGGIE *(calling off)*: Come on, Luke. You ready, Sam?

SAM *(off)*: Right, love. Just cleaning this oil off my hands.

MAGGIE: Not more oil! The day that man dies there'll be oil on his hands. What a man!

LUKE *comes forward. His manner is much younger.*

LUKE: Is this better, mum? I've scrubbed behind my ears, honest.

MAGGIE *(inspecting his ears, neck and hands)*: All right. Let you off this time. But make sure you do it properly in the mornings, young man. Never seen such a tide mark! Better. Look a lot nicer now. More like my lad. In you get.

LUKE *climbs into the car and sits behind the driving-seat.*

MAGGIE: Your dad's still cleaning up. Talk about women being fussy and always late. Your dad can beat them all.

LUKE: Was tinkering with the steering or something, mum.

MAGGIE: This car! If I looked after the house the way he looks after this car, I'd get nothing else done. I hope they don't have cars in heaven or I shall see no more of him there than I've seen here – nothing but his B-T-M sticking from under the bonnet.

She gets into the car and sits in the front passenger seat. Enter SAM LAWSON. *He too is middle-aged. He is wearing a stiff-looking new suit and cloth cap.*

SAM: Do I have to wear this Sunday suit, Maggie? It's as stiff as tin-plate.

MAGGIE: You're not taking it off until we've left town, Sam. Not having you looking your usual scruffy self on a Sunday. At least let the neighbours see you know how to dress proper, even if they only see it on Sundays.

SAM: Are you all ready then?

MAGGIE: We are. We've been ready these past ten minutes.

SAM (*sitting in the driving-seat*): Make sure then. It's you that worries, not me. You said everything was all right last week and we had to come back after half-and-hour to see if you'd switched the oven gas off.

MAGGIE: May your sins be forgiven you, Sam Lawson, for such exaggeration. Now stop your teasing and let's be off.

SAM *goes through the motions of starting the car. We hear it distantly. The noise of the engine accompanies the scene, dream-like.* SAM *drives in mime.* MAGGIE *and* LUKE *watch the passing scene.*

MAGGIE: Mrs Hawthorn got some new curtains, I see.

LUKE: You aren't half nosy, mum.

MAGGIE: Just interested in the folk about me, Luke son, that's all. (*She waves and calls to someone they are passing.*) Billy Turner looking better, Sam. And just look at those leaves bursting out! May is a beautiful month.

SAM (*teasing*): Beautiful!

MAGGIE: You've no eye for nature, Sam Lawson. All you ever think of is oily cars.

SAM: You never object to sitting in this one.

MAGGIE (*popping a sweet into his mouth*): Get on with you!

SAM: Ta, Maggie.

LUKE (*being given his sweet*): Thanks, mum.

SAM (*catching sight of a car ahead*): Look at this one, Luke. The new Jag. (SAM's and LUKE's *heads swivel as the car passes.*) Beauty! Wish we had a car like that, dad.

SAM: Costs money, a car like that, son. Maybe three quid just to keep it on the road.

MAGGIE: Nothing to the fortune you've spent on this one in time alone.

LUKE: How fast will the Jag go, dad?

SAM: Oh – hundred-and-twenty, hundred-and-thirty. Maybe more. But there's not many places in England where you can do it for long.

LUKE: How fast will ours go, dad?

SAM: Sixty maybe. But she'd be a bit of a bone-shaker at that speed.

LUKE: Go on, dad. Open her up and see what happens.

MAGGIE: Now let's have no James Bond stuff, you two.

SAM: James Bond! Don't be an old stick in the mud, Maggie. (*Shuffling up in his seat ready for action.*) All right, son. This is a good long straight stretch and it's clear. Let's see.

MAGGIE: Sam, stop this car at once. I won't be a party to foolishness.

SAM: Shush, Maggie. Sit and enjoy yourself. It'll only happen once in a lifetime in this old crate.

LUKE: Good old dad! Push it up! Woopee!

The noise of the car increases in volume and seems to race faster and faster. MAGGIE *is hanging on, terrified.*

MAGGIE: That's fast enough, Sam. It'll be dangerous any faster.

LUKE: Faster, dad, faster! Sixty . . . sixty-five . . . sixty-eight. Crikey, dad, she's going to do over seventy!

SAM: So she is, son, so she is.

Suddenly there is terror in his face and the noise of screaming brakes.

SAM: The steering's gone!

We see all three tensed and terrified before the noise of a crash and a blackout.

There is silence for a moment in the blackout. Then we hear the sound of an ambulance klaxon wailing. It fades and is replaced by the music. As it increases in volume, the lights return to normal. LUKE is in the car alone. He is slumped over the side, as he might have been after a crash. The others are sitting just as they were, their attention riveted on the car. As the lights come up, PIP stirs quietly and walks up to the car followed by the others. SIMON exits unseen. PIP gets into the driver's seat, half turned to face LUKE. The others group round. They are quiet and uncertain what to do. LUKE raises his head as the music fades.

LUKE: So it was my fault, you see. I wasn't even hurt . . . hardly a scratch . . . just shocked. And mum and dad were dead.

PIP (*trying to find the right thing to say*): It wasn't your fault, Luke. You couldn't have helped it.

LUKE: But I needn't have egged him on. Mum was right – it was foolishness.

PIP: Sometimes fun *is* foolish. And sometimes even fun goes wrong. It isn't always our fault, Luke.

PAUL: We're all sorry about your mum and dad, Luke. (*There are murmurs of agreement.*)

LUKE: You've all been great. You know, there's been times since my mum and dad was killed that I've wished that I was killed too. All that upper lip stuff that people tell you at times like that, and taking it like a man – when something happens like it did to me, it's not so easy then. But you've all . . . I dunno . . . sort of brought me back to life again. Yesterday and today, I've enjoyed myself. (*He has got out of the car and is sitting on the front wheel.*)

CHIPS: We've enjoyed it too. We was bored before anyhow. And Eddie isn't always right, is he?

They all stare at EDDIE, *who eyes them a moment. Slowly he walks away, leaving them. He passes* LUKE. *As he does so,* LUKE *catches his arm and pulls him round, gently.*

LUKE: Who is? (*He looks at* EDDIE *a moment, then drops his arm and turns back to the others.*) It was Simon who saved the day really. If he hadn't took all you lot going at him the way he did, I'd have never told you about the crash.

PIP (*looking round for* SIMON): Simon!

The others call out for him. Suddenly he rushes in, and finds himself in front of PAUL. *There is a tense pause. Then* PAUL *smiles.*

PAUL: I'm sorry, Simon. I'm sorry I lost my temper.

Suddenly PAUL *rubs his hand through the oil on* SIMON's *chest and smudges it on his own face.* SIMON *laughs.*

SIMON: That's all right. I've someone who wants to meet you. (*He calls off.*) Mrs Lovejoy!

Enter MRS LOVEJOY.

SIMON: This is Mrs Lovejoy. She's Luke's foster-mother.

MRS LOVEJOY: Hello.

They call their greetings.

PIP: Mrs Lovejoy, we're taking Luke home tonight. Why not come down with us and have a chat to mum. She'd be glad to meet you, I know. And there's so much to talk about.

MRS LOVEJOY: Thanks, Pippa, I will.

PIP: We'll go down and prepare mum for the invasion. You follow with Luke. Come on, you lot.

Exit all but LUKE *and* MRS LOVEJOY. LUKE *is standing in the car, just as he was during the* MAGISTRATE *scene, and* MRS LOVEJOY *comes to him, just as she did then.*

MRS LOVEJOY: Hello, Luke.

LUKE: Hello, Mrs Lovejoy.

MRS LOVEJOY: Nice to have you back, Luke.

LUKE: Thanks. (*He shrugs.*) Sorry about running again.

MRS LOVEJOY: Don't you give it another thought, Luke.

LUKE: I've stopped running now, anyway.

MRS LOVEJOY: I'm glad. There's things you got to live with, things you can't run away from, and you've found that out, and I'm glad.

LUKE: So am I. (*He climbs out of the car and they come together.*) But . . . why did they have to die, Mrs Lovejoy? Why did it have to happen to me? They were good folks, my mum and dad.

MRS LOVEJOY: I don't know, Luke. Why did my Harold have to go so soon? Why ain't I got no kids?

LUKE: Doesn't seem fair somehow.

MRS LOVEJOY: That's what I thought when my Harold went. I've thought about it a lot. But I reckon, son, that it's not the unfairness that matters, and it does no good worritin' on about it. It's all part of something bigger than me or Harold, or you, and your mum and dad. What matters, it seems to me, is other folk, and just seeing each other through as best we can.

LUKE (*smiling at her*): Bit hard that!

MRS LOVEJOY: Aye. But it is the ones who can do it when it's hardest that are happiest and count for most. Come on, or the others will be gone and we not knowing the way. (*She stands back from him and pulls at her clothes.*) Here! Do you think Pip's mum will mind me in these old clothes? Never know what other folk will think!

LUKE (*laughing*): Now, Mrs L. Just relax. Just take what comes!

MRS LOVEJOY (*laughing too now*): Well, Luke, son. I'll try.

MRS LOVEJOY *climbs on to the sky-line and turns to see that he is following.* LUKE *has stopped by the car and is giving it a last look. The music has faded up.* LUKE *pauses a moment, then shrugs before following* MRS LOVEJOY *on to the sky-line. They exit together.*

The lights fade, until once more the car alone is lit. Slowly the light on the car fades and the CURTAIN *falls.*

THE END